LITERACY FOR AGES 10-11 Ten Minute Tests

CONTENTS

Louis Fidge

Some **vowels** in longer words are **not stressed** and are difficult to hear.

envelope

Colour in your score on the testometer!

15
14
13
12
11
10
9
8
7
6
5
4
3
2
1

Fill in the missing vowels.

1. di___mond

2. accident___l

3. entr___nce

4. diff___rent

5. deod___rant

6. myst___ry

7. cru___l

8. int___resting

9. eff___rt

10. monast___ry

11. lunch___on

12. sep___rate

13. butt___n

14. skel___ton

15. ph___tographer

A **root word** is a word to which **prefixes** or **suffixes** may be added. Sometimes the root word is **easy** to see. Sometimes the root word is **harder** to work out.

bicycle (root word = cycle)

beautiful (root word = beauty)

Colour in your score on the testometer!

Work out the root word for each of these words.

1. befriend _____

2. assistance _____

3. centimetre _____

4. disability _____

5. beggar _____

6. engineer _____

7. exchange _____

8. kingdom _____

9. brightness _____

10. imperfect _____

11. prefix _____

12. service _____

13. superman _____

14. duckling _____

15. withhold _____

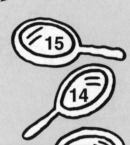
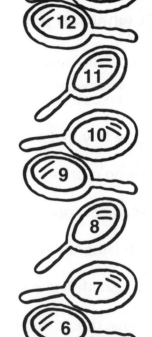
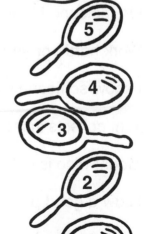

A **dash** holds words apart. It is stronger than a comma but is not as strong as a full stop.

Colour in your score on the testometer!

I have got a new bike – a mountain bike.

Decide where to put the dash in each sentence.

1. I had my favourite meal   spaghetti.

2. I love apples   Ben hates them!

3. One boy looked strange   he was wearing a mask.

4. I won a prize   for coming first in spelling.

5. My uncle appeared   laughing as usual.

6. Christopher Wren built a famous cathedral   St Paul's.

7. Mr Smith has a sports car   a silver one.

8. I love music   especially pop music.

9. On the sand I found something interesting   an old chest.

10. Work hard   or you will never get a good job!

11. I know someone very brave   my friend Sarah.

12. Tom collects insects   especially beetles.

13. Mount Pico is in the Azores   a group of islands.

14. I saw a good programme last night   a monster film.

15. My room overlooks a wood   a small dark wood.

15
14
13
12
11
10
9
8
7
6
5
4
3
2
1

English is not just **one language**. It is made up of words taken from many **other languages**.

Colour in your score on the testometer!

pizza (Italian)   yacht (Dutch)   vase (French)

Find the words we have borrowed from other languages.

ballerina	skipper	buffet	piano	cabaret
bracket	spaghetti	sketch	schooner	bouquet
opera	confetti	smuggle	landscape	duvet

The words from Italy all end in a vowel other than **e**.

1. _____   2. _____   3. _____

4. _____   5. _____

The words from France all end in **et**.

6. _____   7. _____   8. _____

9. _____   10. _____

The other words are all Dutch words.

11. _____   12. _____   13. _____

14. _____   15. _____

A **mnemonic** is a way of remembering the spelling of tricky words.

OoooH

I have **a che**st ache

Colour in your score on the testometer!

ambitious   believe   business   breadth

cereal   chocolate   conscience   government

island   knowledge   mathematics

piece   separate   soldier   whole

Find the word with the following word 'hiding' in it.

1. know _____
2. lie _____
3. them _____
4. pie _____
5. bit _____
6. late _____
7. bus _____
8. men _____
9. rat _____
10. bread _____
11. science _____
12. who _____
13. is _____
14. real _____
15. die _____

Punctuation marks help us make sense of what we read. Where we put punctuation marks can make a difference!

I wore a hat. On my head. I wore some boots.

I wore a hat on my head. I wore some boots.

Colour in your score on the testometer!

Fill in the missing punctuation mark.

1. Dr Turner__s car was green.

2. Mrs Brown, who was getting angry__ shouted loudly.

3. "Don__t cross the busy road," Mrs Smith warned Tom.

4. Do you like oranges or lemons best__

5. During the night__ it rained heavily.

6. "Where's my dinner?__ the giant roared.

7. "I hate sprouts__" Sam shouted.

8. My brother hates music__ but I love it.

9. In my pocket I had a coin, a sweet__ a tissue and a badge.

10. The teachers__ room is next to the office.

11. Where are you going__

12. I__m nearly eleven.

13. The film doesn__t begin for an hour.

14. "Hands up__" the robber shouted.

15. __My job can be dangerous," the police officer said.

The English language has been influenced by **many other languages**. Understanding the **origins** of words sometimes helps us to spell them.

The word **phone** comes from a Greek word meaning **sound**.

microphone   telephone

spectator   liberty   signal   liberal   spectacles
audience   liberate   audible   script   signature
describe   scribble   spectacular   auditorium   design

Write some English words we get from these Latin words.

signum (meaning a sign)

1. _____   2. _____   3. _____

liber (meaning free)

4. _____   5. _____   6. _____

audio (meaning I hear)

7. _____   8. _____   9. _____

scribo (meaning I write)

10. _____   11. _____   12. _____

specto (meaning I watch)

13. _____   14. _____   15. _____

A **clause** is a **group of words** which can be used as a **whole sentence** or as **part of a sentence**. Many sentences contain **more than one** clause.

Colour in your score on the testometer!

This sentence contains two clauses.
The stars twinkled and the moon shone.
⌐— clause 1 —⌐   ⌐— clause 2 —⌐

Write and say how many clauses there are in each sentence. (1 or 2)

1. I like West Highland Terrier dogs. _____

2. Some cats stay out all night. _____

3. I fell over while we were playing. _____

4. The cat chased the birds that landed on the grass. _____

5. I posted the letter in the post box. _____

6. I bought the comic from the shop. _____

7. When the wind blew the trees swayed. _____

8. Last night I had stomach ache after I ate my tea. _____

9. Cows moo but don't bark. _____

10. Nelson's Column stands in the middle of London. _____

11. The man got stuck when the lift doors closed. _____

12. I went to Spain and visited Madrid. _____

13. My budgie escaped when I left its cage open. _____

14. The lady paid for her hat and left the shop. _____

15. The ugly troll waited patiently under the bridge. _____

A **proverb** is a **wise saying** that has been around for a **long time**.

Colour in your score on the testometer!

Don't count your chickens before they're hatched.

Match up the beginning and ending of each proverb.

1. Absence makes the heart — than words.

2. Beggars can't be — twice shy.

3. Actions speak louder — never.

4. Birds of a feather — less speed.

5. Once bitten, — choosers.

6. Every cloud has — out of mind.

7. Too many cooks — you leap.

8. Don't put all your eggs → grow fonder.

9. More haste, — than one.

10. Make hay while — flock together.

11. Two heads are better — a silver lining.

12. Better late than — in one basket.

13. Look before — the sun shines.

14. Out of sight, — saves nine.

15. A stitch in time — spoil the broth.

Words can be broken down into smaller parts, called **syllables**.

um / brel / la   (3 syllables)

Colour in your score on the testometer!

Think of a suitable second syllable for each word. Write the words you make.

1.   de + ___ + mine = _____

2.   u + ___ + form = _____

3.   hos + ___ + al = _____

4.   ex + ___ + lent = _____

5.   at + ___ + tion = _____

6.   dif + ___ + ent = _____

7.   ad + ___ + ture = _____

8.   syl + ___ + le = _____

9.   par + ___ + chute = _____

10.   in + ___ + duce = _____

11.   be + ___ + ning = _____

12.   e + ___ + tric = _____

13.   Sep + ___ + ber = _____

14.   pun + ___ + ment = _____

15.   fa + ___ + ite = _____

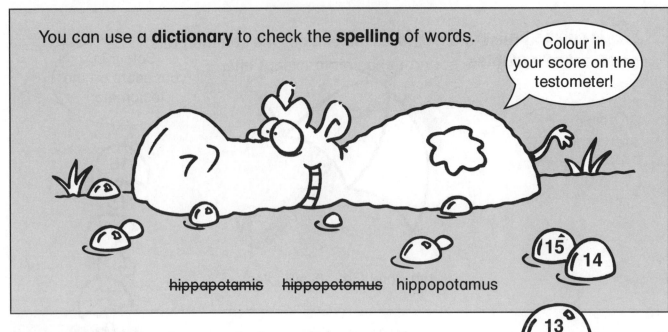

You can use a **dictionary** to check the **spelling** of words.

Colour in your score on the testometer!

~~hippapotamis~~ ~~hippopotomus~~ hippopotamus

Each of the following words is spelt incorrectly.
Write each word correctly. Use a dictionary if necessary.

1. ocasion _____

2. priviledge _____

3. fasinate _____

4. exitement _____

5. immidiate _____

6. reconise _____

7. mathmatics _____

8. dissappear _____

9. controll _____

10. marrage _____

11. rubarb _____

12. temporey _____

13. disasterous _____

14. sissors _____

15. enviroment _____

Test 16 — Spelling rules

Some **spelling rules** are helpful to remember. One common rule is: **i** (when it makes the sound **ee**) before **e** except after **c**.

Colour in your score on the testometer!

I rec**ei**ved a p**ie**ce of cake.

Follow the rule. Choose ie or ei to complete each word.

1. bel____ve

2. rec____ve

3. c____ling

4. ch____f

5. p____ce

6. rel____f

7. f____ld

8. perc____ve

9. dec____ve

10. dec____t

11. lad____s

12. pr____st

13. n____ce

14. f____rce

15. conc____t

15
14
13
12
11
10
9
8
7
6
5
4
3
2
1

A **conditional verb** tells you the action **might** happen (or might have happened), because it **depends** on someone or something else.

Colour in your score on the testometer!

I **would** buy an ice-cream if I had any money.

Say if the conditional verbs in bold indicate the past or future tense.

1. If it stops raining we **might go** out. _____

2. If I had searched I **would have found** my watch. _____

3. She **would have passed** her test if she had tried harder. _____

4. I **might go** to America next year. _____

5. If I had heard the alarm I **would have got** up. _____

6. I **could have saved** my money but I didn't. _____

7. I **might play** cricket tomorrow. _____

8. If I were in charge I **would give** everyone a holiday. _____

9. If you won the Lottery what **would** you **buy**? _____

10. I **could have won** the race if I hadn't fallen over. _____

11. I **should have left** while I had the chance. _____

12. No one **would notice** if you went later. _____

13. How much **would** it **cost** to buy that dress? _____

14. I **would have read** the book if you hadn't disturbed me. _____

15. If you come to town with me I **might buy** you a present. _____

15 14 13 12 11 10 9 8 7 6 5 4 3 2 1

When we write notes we can **abbreviate** some words.

Colour in your score on the testometer!

I come from the USA.
USA = United States of America

Match up each abbreviation with its meaning.

1.	kph	United Nations
2.	dept	note well
3.	PTO	Crescent
4.	UN	kilometres per hour
5.	Rd	Her (or His) Royal Highness
6.	anon	please reply
7.	etc	Member of Parliament
8.	NB	department
9.	RSVP	Road
10.	BC	please turn over
11.	Sq	Before Christ
12.	Cresc	United Kingdom
13.	MP	anonymous
14.	UK	Square
15.	HRH	etcetera

Our language is **changing** all the time. Words **fall out of use** and **new words** enter our language.

Colour in your score on the testometer!

A **cobbler** made shoes. We no longer use this word much.

An **astronaut** flies in space. This is a new space-age word.

Match up these old words with their meanings.

1. frock — hat
2. quaff — drinking cup
3. bonnet → dress
4. satchel — container for coal
5. guinea — drink
6. tinker — an old coin
7. goblet — schoolbag
8. scuttle — a man who mended pots

Complete these new 'computer' words.

9. mon___ ___or

10. m___ ___em

11. key___ ___ ___rd

12. e-m___ ___ ___

13. ___ous___

14. inter___ ___ ___

15. w___bs___ ___ ___

15
14
13
12
11
10
9
8
7
6
5
4
3
2
1

Hi! How's it going?

THIEVES WILL BE PROSECUTED.

Colour in your score on the testometer!

We speak to each other **informally**.   **Official language** is more **formal**.

Match up the formal words or phrases with their informal meanings.

1. forename
2. marital status
3. block letters
4. nationality
5. occupation
6. I beg you pardon.
7. Entrance forbidden!
8. duplicate
9. beverages
10. consume
11. on the reverse
12. renumeration
13. dwelling
14. Smoking prohibited!
15. append

capital letters

the work you do

drinks

on the back

first name

No smoking

whether you are married or single

pay

what country you come from

sorry

eat

attach

You are not allowed in.

where you live

a copy

15
14
13
12
11
10
9
8
7
6
5
4
3
2
1

We can often change a **root word** by adding a **prefix**.

We can often change a **root word** by adding a **suffix**.

Colour in your score on the testometer!

discomfort ← comfort → comfortable
(root word + prefix)   (root word)   (root word + suffix)

Choose the correct prefix to complete each word.

1. ____board   (a/be)

2. ____loved   (a/be)

3. ____mature   (in/im)

4. ____considerate   (in/im)

5. ____legible   (ir/il)

6. ____responsible   (ir/il)

7. ____noculars   (bi/tri)

8. ____dent   (bi/tri)

Work out the root word of each of these words.

9.   accidentally   _____

10. clumsily   _____

11. suspicious   _____

12. angry   _____

13. circular   _____

14. metallic   _____

15. sensible   _____

15
14
13
12
11
10
9
8
7
6
5
4
3
2
1

A **complex sentence** contains a **main clause** and a **subordinate** (less important) **clause**. The subordinate clause may not make sense on its own.

Colour in your score on the testometer!

The detective arrested the man ⟵——— main clause ———⟶ | who had robbed the bank. ⟵— subordinate clause —⟶

Join up each main clause with a sensible subordinate clause.

1. The children started talking   although I watered them.

2. Tom's mum was cross   because the gate was open.

3. The flowers did not grow   where I saw huge skyscrapers.

4. I visited New York   when the teacher went out.

5. The dog escaped   which I had lost.

6. It often rains   when she saw his messy bedroom.

7. I found the key   so I always carry an umbrella.

Now try these.

8. I had a bath   before she left.

9. The audience cheered   because it was starving.

10. My aunt hugged me   who is very naughty.

11. The lady asked the way   because I was so muddy.

12. Abdi is the boy   when she got lost.

13. Mrs Cane won the Lottery   before it got dark.

14. The child ran home   when the band played.

15. The dog ate hungrily   so she bought a new house.

A **clause** may be used either as a **whole sentence** or as **part of a sentence**. A clause always contains a **verb**.

A **phrase** does **not** contain a **verb**. A phrase does **not make sense** on its own.

Colour in your score on the testometer!

The balloon popped   with a loud bang.
↑___ clause ___↑   ↑___ phrase ___↑

Write whether each of these is a clause or a phrase.

1. Sarah slipped over. _____

2. in a muddy puddle _____

3. after the programme _____

4. Sam rode her bike. _____

5. The spacecraft landed on the hill. _____

6. as fast as a flash _____

7. The lady put down her bag. _____

8. until next time _____

9. The lion pounced on the gazelle. _____

10. near the lake _____

11. until midnight _____

12. The baby smiled at me. _____

13. Some cars have big boots. _____

14. all green and slimy _____

15. A giraffe has a long neck. _____

It is important to check that your **punctuation** is correct.

DANGER.
NO SWIMMING ALLOWED

DANGER?
NO. SWIMMING ALLOWED.

Colour in your score on the testometer!

Fill in the missing punctuation marks.

1. The monkeys were playing in the tree___

2. Amir bought eggs___ milk, bread and flour at the shop.

3. "Where do you live___" she asked.

4. "Get out___" he shouted.

5. The dog___s tail was wagging.

6. ___What book are you reading?" Shiraz asked.

7. After tea___ Mark watched TV.

8. Mrs Best said___ "Where is my bag?"

9. It isn___t a nice day.

10. The toy didn___t cost much.

11. "Come with me___ Ben," the teacher said.

12. "Stop that at once___" Mr Khan demanded.

13. The dog, a small poodle___ yapped loudly.

14. The door was open___ inviting him to enter.

15. "When I___ve got enough money, I'll retire," Mr Farr said.

When a word has one vowel before a single final consonant, we double the consonant before adding a **suffix** – if the last syllable is stressed.

Colour in your score on the testometer!

begin - beginning

Add the suffix ing. **Write the word you make.**

1. rebel _____

2. admit _____

3. forget _____

4. prefer _____

5. signal _____

Add the suffix ed. **Write the word you make.**

6. regret _____

7. transmit _____

8. travel _____

9. occur _____

10. control _____

Take the suffix off. **Write the root word you are left with.**

11. fulfilled _____

12. forbidding _____

13. referred _____

14. marvelled _____

15. omitting _____

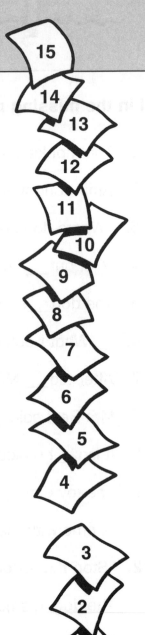

win

Short vowels make the **sound** of the letter.

wine

Long vowels say the **name** of the letter.

Colour in your score on the testometer!

Use the signs to show whether the vowels are long ⁻ or short ˘ .

1. sigh

2. plush

3. truth

4. wild

5. swam

6. desk

7. show

8. shy

9. flip

10. drip

11. text

12. stay

13. most

14. blind

15. lost

It is helpful to learn the spelling of **common word endings**.

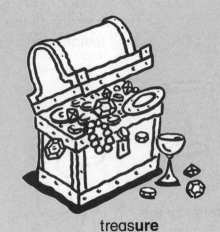

treas**ure**

col**our**

Colour in your score on the testometer!

Choose our **or** ure **to complete each word.**

1. flav_____

2. cult_____

3. furnit_____

4. fav_____

5. mixt_____

6. hon_____

7. vap_____

8. inj_____

9. lab_____

10. col_____

11. fig_____

12. fail_____

13. vig_____

14. harb_____

15. capt_____

15
14
13
12
11
10
9
8
7
6
5
4
3
2
1

It is helpful to learn the spelling of **common word endings**.

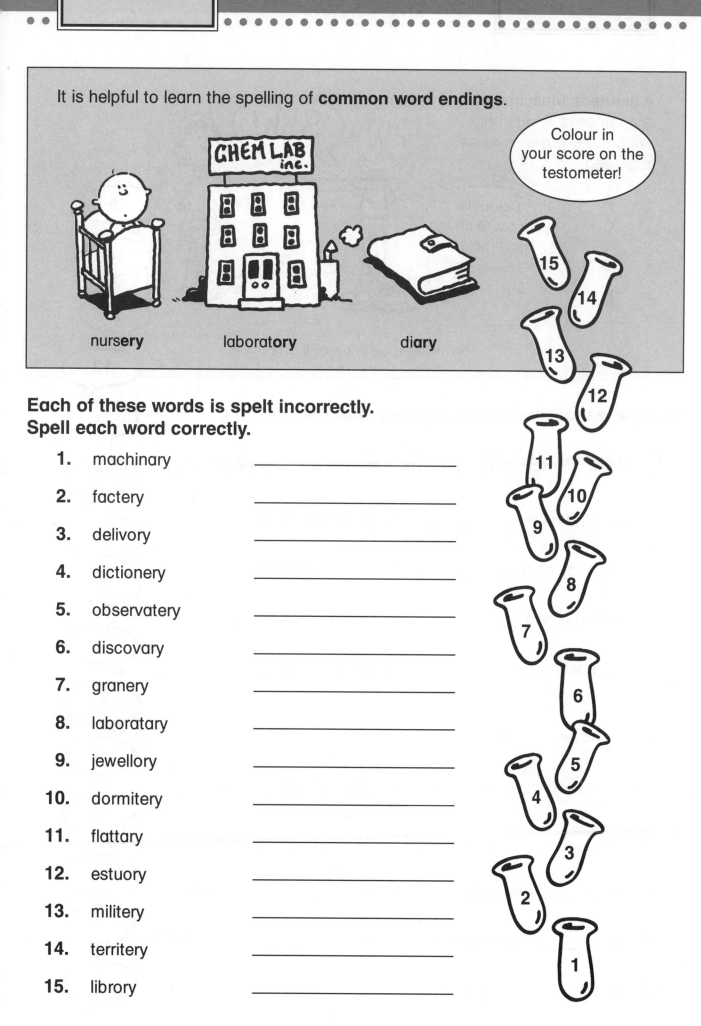

Colour in your score on the testometer!

nurs**ery**   laborat**ory**   di**ary**

Each of these words is spelt incorrectly.
Spell each word correctly.

1. machinary _____

2. factery _____

3. delivory _____

4. dictionery _____

5. observatery _____

6. discovary _____

7. granery _____

8. laboratary _____

9. jewellory _____

10. dormitery _____

11. flattary _____

12. estuory _____

13. militery _____

14. territery _____

15. librory _____

A **simile** is when one thing is compared to another. We often use the word **as** in similes.

Colour in your score on the testometer!

The children were **as** quiet **as** mice.

Complete these well-known similes with these words.

| tortoise | swan | bat | fox | ox | mule | lion | elephant |

1. as blind as a _____
2. as obstinate as a _____
3. as crafty as a _____
4. as heavy as an _____
5. as fierce as a _____
6. as strong as an _____
7. as graceful as a _____
8. as slow as a _____

Now do these.

| thin | regular | fit | easy | safe | flat | sour |

9. as _____ as a fiddle
10. as _____ as vinegar
11. as _____ as a pancake
12. as _____ as a rake
13. as _____ as clockwork
14. as _____ as ABC
15. as _____ as a bank

15
14
13
12
11
10
9
8
7
6
5
4
3
2
1

We can learn a lot by playing **word games**. They can help us with our **spelling** and help to **improve our vocabulary**.

Colour in your score on the testometer!

Use a dictionary to help you work out these clues.

These words all begin with **she**.

1. a law officer _____
2. a place for protection _____
3. very steep _____
4. large scissors _____

These words all begin with **go**.

5. a hairy berry _____
6. a prickly shrub _____
7. glasses for protection _____
8. a young goose _____

These words all begin with **pea**.

9. quiet _____
10. a bird with beautiful feathers _____
11. a kind of fuel _____
12. grows in a pod underground _____

These words all begin with **ant**.

13. old and valuable _____
14. an animal like a deer _____
15. kind of aerial _____

Answers

Test 1

The missing vowels are in **bold**.
1. di**a**mond
2. accident**a**l
3. entr**a**nce
4. diff**e**rent
5. deod**o**rant
6. myst**e**ry
7. cru**e**l
8. int**e**resting
9. eff**o**rt
10. mon**a**st**e**ry
11. lunch**e**on
12. sep**a**rate
13. butt**o**n
14. skel**e**ton
15. ph**o**tographer

Test 2
1. friend
2. assist
3. metre
4. disable
5. beg
6. engine
7. change
8. king
9. bright
10. perfect
11. fix
12. serve
13. man
14. duck
15. hold

Test 3
1. I had my favourite meal – spaghetti.
2. I love apples – Ben hates them!
3. One boy looked strange – he was wearing a mask.
4. I won a prize – for coming first in spelling.
5. My uncle appeared – laughing as usual.
6. Christopher Wren built a famous cathedral – St Paul's.
7. Mr Smith has a sports car – a silver one.
8. I love music – especially pop music.
9. On the sand I found something interesting – an old chest.
10. Work hard – or you will never get a good job!
11. I know someone very brave – my friend Sarah.
12. Tom collects insects – especially beetles.
13. Mount Pico is in the Azores – a group of islands.
14. I saw a good programme last night – a monster film.
15. My room overlooks a wood – a small dark wood.

Test 4
1. <u>door</u>
2. <u>man</u>
3. <u>wind</u>
4. <u>children</u>
5. <u>car</u>
6. <u>ride</u>
7. <u>ate</u>
8. <u>will try</u>
9. <u>cooked</u>
10. <u>cross</u>
11. <u>slippery</u>
12. <u>rough</u>
13. <u>colourful</u>
14. <u>scary</u>
15. <u>favourite</u>

Test 5
1. nevertheless
2. or
3. because
4. as
5. before
6. when
7. so that
8. if
9. then
10. in case
11. until
12. however
13. but
14. as soon as
15. because

Test 6

Answers 1-8: the correct prefix is in **bold**.
1. **auto**graph
2. **il**legal
3. **de**port
4. **im**patient
5. **dis**approve
6. **mis**behave
7. **em**bark
8. **pre**arrange
9. confidence
10. bakery
11. communication
12. student
13. replacement
14. service
15. friendliness

Test 7
1. active
2. passive
3. active
4. passive
5. passive
6. active
7. active
8. passive
9. active
10. passive
11. active
12. active
13. passive
14. passive
15. active

Test 8
1. ballerina
2. piano
3. spaghetti
4. opera
5. confetti
6. buffet
7. cabaret
8. bracket
9. bouquet
10. duvet
11. skipper
12. sketch
13. schooner
14. smuggle
15. landscape

Test 9
1. knowledge
2. believe
3. mathematics
4. piece
5. ambitious
6. chocolate
7. business
8. government
9. separate
10. breadth
11. conscience
12. whole
13. island
14. cereal
15. soldier

Test 10

The missing punctuation marks are in **bold**.
1. Dr Turner**'**s car was green.
2. Mrs Brown**,** who was getting angry**,** shouted loudly.
3. **"**Don't cross the busy road**,"** Mrs Smith warned Tom.
4. Do you like oranges or lemons best**?**
5. During the night**,** it rained heavily.
6. **"**Where's my dinner?**"** the giant roared.
7. **"**I hate sprouts!**"** Sam shouted.
8. My brother hates music – but I love it.
9. In my pocket I had a coin**,** a sweet**,** a tissue and a badge.
10. The teachers**'** room is next to the office.
11. Where are you going**?**
12. I**'**m nearly eleven.
13. The film doesn**'**t begin for an hour.
14. **"**Hands up!**"** the robber shouted.
15. **"**My job can be dangerous**,"** the police officer said.

Test 11
1. signal
2. signature
3. design
4. liberty
5. liberal
6. liberate
7. audience
8. audible
9. auditorium
10. script
11. describe
12. scribble
13. spectator
14. spectacles
15. spectacular

Test 12
1. 1
2. 1
3. 2
4. 2
5. 1
6. 1
7. 2
8. 2
9. 2
10. 1
11. 2
12. 2
13. 2
14. 2
15. 1

Test 13
1. grow fonder
2. choosers
3. than words
4. flock together
5. twice shy
6. a silver lining
7. spoil the broth
8. in one basket
9. less speed
10. the sun shines
11. than one
12. never
13. you leap
14. out of mind
15. saves nine

Test 14

The missing second syllable is in **bold**.
1. de**ter**mine
2. **uni**form
3. hos**pit**al
4. ex**cell**ent
5. at**ten**tion
6. **diff**erent
7. ad**ven**ture
8. **syll**able
9. **para**chute
10. **intro**duce
11. be**ginn**ing
12. e**lec**tric
13. Sep**tem**ber
14. pun**ish**ment
15. fa**vour**ite